Basic Electronics
Meters
Voltage-dividers

Basic Electronics is published in five parts:

Book 1 — sections A and B
Introducing Electronics. Measuring Instruments

Book 2 — sections C and D
Resistors in Circuits. Capacitors in Circuits

Book 3 — sections E and F
Inductors in Circuits. Diodes in Circuits

Book 4 — sections G and H
Meters. Voltage-dividers

Book 5 — sections I, J, and K
Transistors in Circuits. Transistors in Action. Post-transistor Projects

The course was prepared by Malcolm Plant, a member of the central team of Project Technology, and stems from earlier work on the teaching of electronics by Douglas Shorthouse.

Basic Electronics

Book 4 **Meters**
Voltage-dividers

 The English Universities Press Ltd/
Schools Council

CONTENTS

Section G: Meters

Section H: Voltage-dividers

Section G
Meters

G1 WHY WE NEED ELECTRICAL METERS

G1.1 How electric current could be detected

There is often very little evidence for current flow in a circuit; there may be no obvious movement, no flashing lights, and no noise to indicate that electrical energy is being utilised. Touching the components will not be very helpful. Certainly the dissipation of electrical energy as heat does make components such as resistors slightly warmer than the surroundings, but, besides the danger of electrocution, no respectable electronics enthusiast would use this method for measuring current or voltage.

1 You have used a flashlight bulb to indicate current. What disadvantages does it have for the measurement of current?

Most bulbs require fairly high currents before they glow. In any case, they show only that current flows when the filament can be *seen* to glow; they do not tell you the current direction or its strength very accurately. You may be able to think of other ways of detecting the flow of electrons in a circuit.

2 Could you use the *magnetic field* caused by a current to detect and measure the strength of the current?

G1.2 Using the magnetic effect of a current

Current flowing through a coil of wire produces a magnetic field — you have studied this effect in the section concerned with inductors. But, in order to use the magnetic effect, the current-generated magnetic field must be made to react

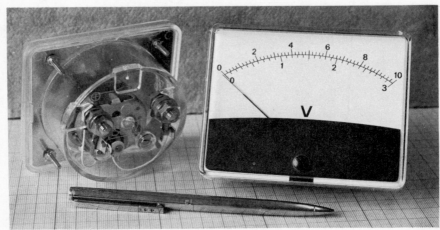

Fig. G1.1 A general view of a moving-coil meter.

2

with another magnetic field. In the *moving-coil meter,* a current flowing through a coil causes the coil to twist in the magnetic field provided by a permanent magnet. This principle is used as the basis of an electric motor, and is often referred to as the *'motor effect'.*

Fig. G1.1 shows the face of an RS Components Ltd moving-coil panel meter. It is marked in two ranges. It requires $100\,\mu A$ to give a *full-scale-deflection (f.s.d.)* and, in order to measure 3 V f.s.d. or 10 V f.s.d., it requires external multipliers (see Section G8). Also shown is the rear view of a 1 mA f.s.d. panel meter. Note that these meters have two terminals, one marked + and one marked −, which indicates that they are used in direct-current circuits.

G2 THE PARTS OF A MOVING-COIL METER

G2.1 The main parts

The plan outline of a moving-coil meter is shown in fig. G2.1. Use this outline to note the main parts of a meter which is used for electronic work.

1 Note the units in which the scale is divided. Does it measure amperes, volts, or ohms — or any other electrical quantity?

2 If you can see the coil, from what kind of wire do you think it is wound?

3 How does the current enter and leave the coil?

4 What is the purpose of the spiral springs?

5 Which way should the coil twist when current passes through the coil?

6 What is the shape of the permanent magnet? There are specially shaped pole-pieces to this magnet; of what are they made, and why are they designed in this way?

7 What is the purpose of the adjusting screw, and how does it work?

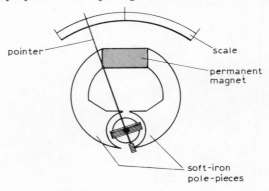

Fig. G2.1 The main parts of a moving-coil meter.

G2.2 The magnetic forces

When current flows through the coil, a magnetic field is produced around it. The strength of this field depends on the strength of the current which flows through the coil. Hence the twisting forces acting on the coil increase with the current — these forces are shown in fig. G2.2.

1 What forces act to stop the coil rotating?

2 How far would the coil twist before coming to rest if the spiral springs were not present?

4

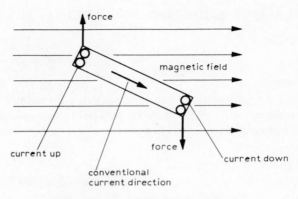

Fig. G2.2 How a force acts on the coil

3 Is the scale of your meter a linear one? That **is**, do equal increases of
current produce equal deflections of the pointer?

G2.3 What makes the scale linear?

One of the advantages of the moving-coil meter is that the deflection of the
pointer is *directly proportional* to the current flowing through the coil. This
means that equal increases of current produce equal increases of deflection. The
scale is therefore *linear,* as you will notice from the meters at hand. The major
factors in the design which make the scale linear are the concave pole-pieces and
the fixed soft-iron core to the coil. These produce what is known as a *radial*
magnetic field in which the coil rotates. Fig. G2.3 shows the position of the two
spiral springs which are used to lead the current in and out of the coil. The coil,
springs, and bearings are known as the *movement* of the meter.

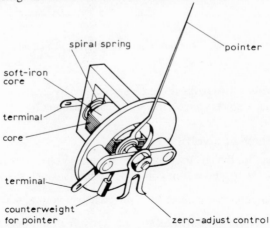

Fig. G2.3 The positions of the spiral springs.

G3 THE PLACE OF AMMETERS AND VOLTMETERS IN A CIRCUIT

G3.1 Reminder

We shall restrict ourselves to discussing only two kinds of moving-coil meter for the present: *ammeters* and *voltmeters*. Your previous experiments should have shown you the place of these meters in a circuit.

G3.2 The place of an ammeter

Ammeters measure the current flow in *amperes*. Ammeters must therefore be connected in *series* with the circuit components *through* which it is required to measure the current flow.

1 What is it that actually flows?

Look at fig. G3.1. The current through R is required. A break is made in the circuit, and an ammeter is connected in *series* with R.

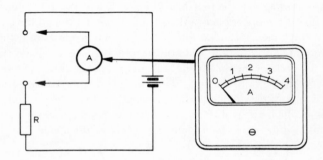

Fig. G3.1 The position of an ammeter in a circuit.

2 If the current through R is not to be changed by inserting the ammeter, should the ammeter have a low or a high resistance?

G3.3 The place of a voltmeter

Voltmeters measure the electrical pressure in *volts*. Voltmeters must therefore be placed in *parallel* with the circuit components *across* which the voltage is required.

1 What is an alternative name for a difference in voltage across a component?

Look at fig. G3.2. The potential difference across R is required; hence the voltmeter is connected in parallel with R.

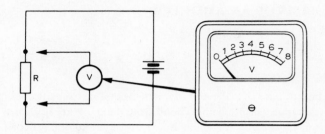

Fig. G3.2 The position of a voltmeter in a circuit.

2 If the current through R (and hence the voltage across it) is not to be changed by the connection of the voltmeter, should the voltmeter have a high or a low resistance?

G3.4 Summary

Ammeters must have a low resistance and voltmeters must have a high resistance if they are to measure current and voltage in a circuit without disturbing the size of these quantities.

G4 THE BASIS OF AN AMMETER

G4.1 The resistance of the coil

It is important to note that the coil of a moving-coil instrument does not have a negligible resistance, despite being wound from copper wire. In fact, the resistance of the coil can vary from a few ohms to several thousand ohms, depending on the design and purpose of the meter.

G4.2 Calculating the current in a simple circuit

So that you can understand the effect of connecting an ammeter in a circuit, work out the following simple calculations based on fig. G4.1.

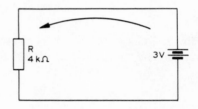

Fig. G4.1 What current flows?

1 What is the current through R? Express your answer in mA.

2 What is the voltage across R?

G4.3 Connecting an ammeter in the circuit

Fig. G4.2 shows a milliammeter which can read 1 mA at full-scale deflection (f.s.d.) The coil of this meter has a resistance of 50 ohms and is connected in series with the 4 kΩ resistor.

1 What is the total resistance in series with the supply?

2 What is the current now flowing through R?

3 What is the current now flowing through the meter?

4 What is the voltage across R?

Note that this ammeter has a negligible effect on the current through R, but only because the ammeter's resistance is low. The smaller the resistance of the coil of the ammeter, the smaller the ammeter's effect on the current it is measuring. All ammeters must have a low resistance.

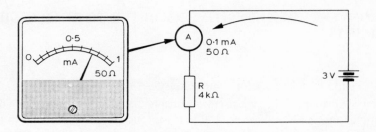

Fig. G4.2 Calculate the new current flowing.

G4.4 Measuring small currents

Some moving-coil meters respond to currents as small as a few microamperes (μA).

1 What fraction of an ampere is a microampere? What fraction of an ampere is a milliampere?

A typical multimeter, which is discussed later in this chapter, will have several current ranges. Its most sensitive range is determined by the intended use of the instrument and the need for it to withstand average wear and tear.

1 A d.c. meter has two terminals, one marked black (−) and one marked red (+).
Which terminal of the meter would you connect to R in fig. G4.2?

G4.5 How to connect a d.c. ammeter in a circuit

Note that, whereas you connect cells in series by joining a positive terminal to a negative terminal of another cell, ammeters are connected so that the *red* terminal leads to the *positive* pole of the battery.

G5 CONVERTING A SENSITIVE AMMETER TO READ HIGHER CURRENTS

G5.1 Protecting the meter's movement

The coil of an ammeter has a resistance which is fixed at a particular value during its manufacture; it is not possible to alter it without rewinding the coil — a tricky and unnecessary task. This resistance and other design factors might produce an instrument having, say, an f.s.d. of $500\,\mu A$.

1 Express $500\,\mu A$ in mA.

If this meter is placed in a circuit which has a current of 0.5 A flowing through it, the coil will *burn out*.

2 What actually burns out? What other damage would be caused?

Certainly a new coil would be required, necessitating a costly repair or a new meter. Some multimeters may have an automatic *cut-out* which automatically *open-circuits* the meter if a current flows which is much greater than that giving f.s.d. Other types are automatically protected from being overloaded by diodes connected across the coil.

3 Examine the operation of automatic cut-out on an Avometer (see Section B).

4 If you wished to measure currents in the range 0.2 to 0.8 A, which one of the following meters would you choose: (a) $5\,\mu A$? (b) 1 A? (c) 500 mA? (d) 0.5 A f.s.d.?

If in doubt about the magnitude of the current to be measured, always choose a meter having the highest f.s.d., in order to reduce the possibility of damage to the meter.

G5.2 The basic method for converting ammeters

It is possible to arrange for a sensitive meter to read a higher current than the movement will allow. To understand how this is done, you will need to revise simple calculations based on the equation $V = I \times R$. Look at fig. G5.1.

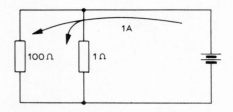

Fig. G5.1 More current through the smaller-value resistor.

1 Are the resistors in series or parallel?

2 Is the voltage across them the same or different?

3 Which resistor carries the largest current?

4 Does this suggest a method for converting a milliammeter to one reading amperes?

If a 1 mA f.s.d meter is to be converted into an instrument giving an f.s.d when 1 A passes through the circuit, a *shunt* is required. The shunt is connected *across* the terminals of the meter, as shown in fig. G5.2.

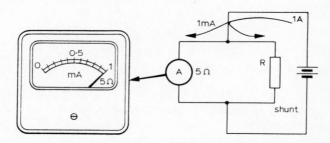

Fig. G5.2 Shunting current from a meter by connecting a low-value resistor across its terminals.

5 If 1 mA is to flow through the meter, how much current flows through the shunt?

G5.3 A formula for calculating shunt values

It is important for you to realise that, if the above meter requires only 1 mA to make it register f.s.d., then, in a circuit in which 1 A flows, 999 mA must pass through the shunt.

The ratio of the current through the meter to the current through the shunt is the reverse ratio of their resistances. This is written as

$$\frac{\text{current through coil}}{\text{current through shunt}} = \frac{\text{resistance of shunt}}{\text{resistance of meter coil}}$$

Thus, in the case of the example in fig. G5.2, where the meter coil has a resistance of 5 Ω.

$$\frac{1}{999} = \frac{R}{5} \text{ or } R = \frac{5}{999} \; \Omega \text{ (approximately 0.005 } \Omega\text{)}$$

This calculation should be clear from the relationship $V = I \times R$.

Since the voltage across the shunt = the voltage across the coil, then ($I \times R$) for shunt = ($I \times R$) for coil. The scale is read as follows: divide all scale readings by 10.

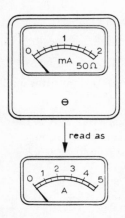

Fig. G5.3 Converting the readings of a milliammeter to amperes.

1 For the meter of fig. G5.3, calculate the shunt resistance if the meter is to measure an f.s.d. of 5 A.

2 How do you read the scale of this meter?

You may use the equation $R_S = R_C/(N - 1)$ to calculate the shunt resistance R_S when you know the coil resistance, R_C, and the number of times, N, by which the scale reading must be multiplied to give the required scale.

G5.4 Experiment: investigating how an ammeter affects current

Assemble the circuit shown in fig. G5.4 on S-DeC or another suitable assembly board. Make sure that the ammeter is correctly connected to the battery.

1 Record the ammeter reading.

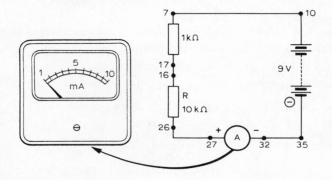

Fig. G5.4 Experimental circuit for finding how an ammeter affects current flow.

12

2 Remove the 10 kΩ resistor R and replace it by one of 5.6 kΩ. Record the new current.

The current which flows is calculated from $I = V/R$. For example, the two resistors have a combined series value of 11 kΩ in the first case; therefore, the current = V/R = 9 V/11 kΩ = 0.82 mA.

3 Next replace the 5.6 kΩ resistor by ones of 1 kΩ, 560 Ω, and 100 Ω in turn and enter the observed and calculated currents in a copy of the table shown.

R (Ω)	calculated current (mA)	observed current (mA)
10k	0.82	
5.6k		
1k		
560		
100		

You will probably have already realised that you have not included the resistance of the meter in your calculations. You will find that the observed and calculated values of the current do not agree. In fact, as the value of R decreases, the difference between the two values increases. This is partly due to not knowing the exact values of the resistors that you use, and to not knowing the precise e.m.f. of the battery. But it is also in greater part due to the fact that, when R is small, the meter resistance becomes more important relative to the value of R.

The results of this experiment stress two very important points about ammeters:

a) an ammeter reduces the current which it is intended to measure;

b) suitable meters must have a resistance which is much smaller than the resistance of the circuit in which the current flows.

G6 THE CONSTRUCTION OF SHUNTS FOR AMMETERS

G6.1 The coil resistance must be known

Suppose that you have a 1 mA f.s.d. meter available and you wish to make shunts for it to enable it to measure 10 mA and 100 mA f.s.d. You must first find the resistance of the coil of the meter. This resistance is often given on the dial of the meter. If the resistance is not given, then it may be found from a simple bridge circuit (Section H), a resistance substitution box (Section C), or a multimeter (Section C).

Suppose you find that the meter has a coil resistance of 100 Ω. Then, for the 10 mA range, the scale multiplying factor is 10 times, and the equation in Section G5.3 predicts that you require a shunt resistance of 11.1 Ω. Similarly, the shunt resistance required for the 100 mA range is 1.01 Ω. This information now enables you to wind the shunt coil.

G6.2 Choosing the wire for the shunt

Some fine copper wire or some resistance wire such as *eureka* or *constantan* is needed. The following table of resistance-wire values will enable you to choose the length of a particular wire that you need. 'Eureka' is an alternative name for constantan.

s.w.g.	diameter		copper		manganin	eureka
	mm	inches	Ω/m	safe current (amperes)	Ω/m	Ω/m
12	2.64	0.1040	0.0032	15.00	0.077	0.089
16	1.63	0.0640	0.0083	6.80	0.204	0.236
20	0.914	0.0360	0.0260	2.60	0.645	0.746
24	0.559	0.0220	0.0700	1.10	1.730	2.000
28	0.376	0.0148	0.1550	0.50	3.820	4.410
30	0.315	0.0124	0.2220	0.40	5.450	6.290
34	0.234	0.0092	0.4040	0.20	9.900	11.400
36	0.193	0.0076	0.5900	0.15	14.500	16.700
40	0.122	0.0048	1.4800	0.06	36.300	42.000

A length slightly longer than that required to give the necessary resistance must be cut, so that connections can be made. If the wire is not insulated, it must be painted with shellac. Enamelled copper wire need not be treated in this way. Rather than trust entirely to the resistances given in the above table, it is best to measure the resistance with a multimeter or a bridge circuit (Section H).

G6.3 Choosing a coil former

Wooden dowels, e.g. pencils, are useful for the former of the coil. The turns are either glued into place or are bound with Sellotape, leaving short lengths protruding from the ends of the coil (see fig. G6.1). Contact is made to these wires, using *thick* copper connecting leads.

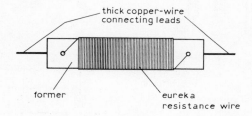

Fig. G6.1 How a shunt might appear.

1 Why should you use thick copper wire to connect the coil to the circuit, and not the same wire as you used for the coil?

G6.4 A multipole switch is required

The two shunts are then soldered into a circuit as shown in fig. G6.2, using a rotary switch to bring each shunt into circuit as required. Fig. G6.3 shows the appearance of the circuit of fig. G6.2: A rear view of the rotary switch is shown, with the lower-resistance coil switched in parallel with the meter terminals by means of the contact C. Contacts A and B allow the 11.1 Ω shunt and the meter without a shunt to be used.

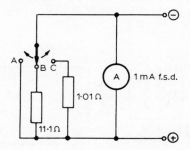

Fig. G6.2 The switching circuit for a three-range ammeter.

1 How many current ranges has this ammeter?

2 What shunt-resistance values would you **require** in order to extend the range to 1 A and 10 A f.s.d.?

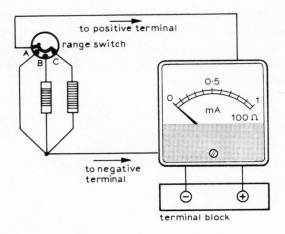

Fig. G6.3 The layout for a three-range ammeter.

G6.5   Checking the accuracy of the meter

You will note that the shunt resistance must be lower the higher the current range to be measured. There is then a problem of constructing and measuring this low resistance, since the resistance of the connecting leads and switch contacts must be taken into account. In these cases, it is very important to use connecting leads which have negligible resistance compared with that of the shunt. In fact, if you construct a simple multirange ammeter like that shown in fig. G6.3, it is best to place it in series with a meter which you know is accurate and adjust the shunt coils until the required f.s.d. is obtained. This arrangement is shown in fig. G6.4.

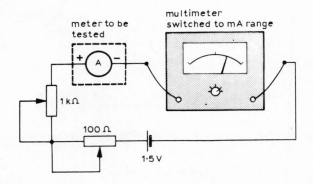

Fig. G6.4 The arrangement for calibrating a home-made ammeter.

G7 THE BASIS OF A VOLTMETER

G7.1 What a voltmeter must do

You have already noted that the ideal voltmeter must have a high resistance so that it measures voltage and yet draws a negligible current from the circuit. As with the ammeters already described, the type of voltmeter considered here is a moving-coil type. The absolutely essential point is that an f.s.d. voltage reading is to be obtained with a minimum of current drawn from the circuit.

  1 If a milliammeter has a resistance of 40 Ω and an f.s.d. of 5 mA, what is the voltage across its terminals at f.s.d.?

Your answer should be 200 mV (0.2 V), which you obtained by using the equation $V = I \times R$. Thus, instead of being calibrated in mA, the meter could be calibrated in mV. However this millivoltmeter draws too large a current from the circuit to which it is connected. To measure such small voltages requires a more sensitive instrument, having a higher coil resistance. For instance, a meter which has a coil resistance of 5 kΩ and gives an f.s.d with a current of 40 μA measures 0.2 V as before, but draws only 40 μA from the circuit to which it is connected.

G7.2 The disadvantage of the basic movement

It is possible to convert the 5 mA, 40 Ω meter into a voltmeter capable of reading greater than 200 mV. To see how this is done, you must first answer the following questions.

  Look at fig. G7.1.

  1 What is the equivalent total resistance of R_1 and R_2?

  2 What is the current flowing through R_1 and R_2?

  3 What is the voltage across R_2?

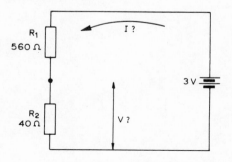

Fig. G7.1 What current flows?

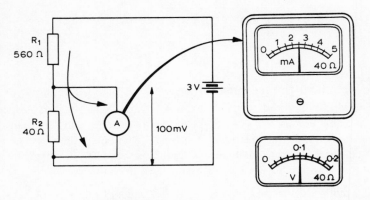

Fig. G7.2 The effect of a low-resistance meter.

Fig. G7.2 shows R_1 and R_2 with a 5 mA, 40 Ω meter across R_2. This meter requires a voltage of 200 mV to give a full-scale deflection, but this does not occur, as it is easy to show.

4 What is the equivalent resistance of R_2 and the meter in fig. G7.2?

The meter and the coil have a combined resistance of half of the resistance of R_2 alone; thus the total resistance across the supply is lowered to 580 Ω (560 Ω + 20 Ω).

5 What is the voltage across R_2 now?

You will see that the voltage is reduced to 20 X 3/580 or approximately 100 mV. Thus, although without the meter it was known that there was a voltage of 0.2 V across the meter, the presence of the meter reduced this to almost half f.s.d. This is a very large error between the voltage expected and the voltage actually measured. As you will see in Section G8, the solution to the problem of measuring voltage is to use a meter which has a *high* resistance.

G8 CONVERTING A MILLIAMMETER TO A VOLTMETER

G8.1 The effect of increasing the meter resistance

Fig. G8.1 is similar to fig. G7.2 but the milliammeter now has a resistance of
200 Ω.

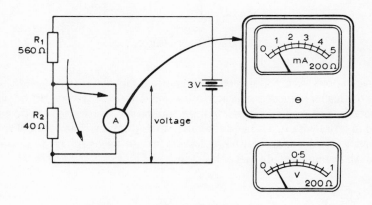

Fig. G8.1 Less current flows through a high-resistance meter.

1 Prove that the voltage across R_2 and the meter is 170 mV.

Thus, increasing the resistance of the meter increases the meter reading to more
nearly the 200 mV it should read; 170 mV is indicated on the meter dial shown in
fig. G8.1. You will notice that, in contrast to the meter described in Section G7,
the meter not only registers more nearly the voltage to be measured, but the
current passing through it is reduced.

G8.2 Using a multiplier

In practice, the resistance of a milliammeter or a microammeter is increased by
the use of a *multiplier*. This is a high-value resistor connected in series with the
meter. In order to understand how a multiplier works, you must answer the
following questions based on fig. G8.2.

1 Calculate the voltage across R_1 and R_2 in the following cases:
   (a) $R_1 = 10\,\Omega$, $R_2 = 1000\,\Omega$; (b) $R_1 = 100\,\Omega$, $R_2 = 1000\,\Omega$;
   (c) $R_1 = 10\,k\Omega$, $R_2 = 10\,\Omega$.

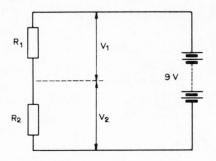

Fig. G8.2 Dividing up a battery voltage.

The calculations should show you one important fact about two resistors in series: the higher voltage occurs across the higher resistor. To convert a milli-voltmeter to one reading a higher voltage requires a high resistance to be connected in series with it. This enables most of the voltage to be measured to be dropped across this series resistance, leaving just sufficient voltage to operate the meter. An example should make this clear.

G8.3   An example of conversion

Suppose a milliammeter having an f.s.d of 5 mA and a coil resistance of 40 Ω is to be converted to a 10 V f.s.d. meter as shown in fig. G8.3.

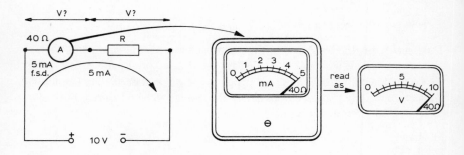

Fig. G8.3 The series circuit of a milliammeter converted to a voltmeter.

1 What is the voltage across the terminals of the meter at f.s.d.?

2 What voltage must occur across R to give f.s.d. on the meter?

3 What current flows through R at f.s.d.?

4 What must be the resistance of R?

You should have calculated that a series resistance of 1960 Ω is required. The total resistance offered by the coil and multiplier is 2 kΩ but, even so, 5 mA is required to give f.s.d. This high current could be reduced by using a more sensitive meter, for example one giving an f.s.d. with a terminal voltage of a few millivolts.

5 What is the value of the multiplier resistance which is required to convert the meter shown in fig. G8.4 to a 0–10 V voltmeter? How do you read the scale?

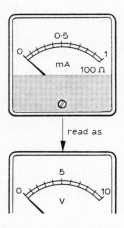

Fig. G8.4 Converting the readings of a milliammeter to volts.

The following formula can be used to calculate multiplier resistor values:

$$R_m = R_c (N - 1)$$

where R_m is the multiplier resistance, R_c is the coil resistance, and N is the number of times by which the scale reading must be multiplied to give the required scale.

G8.4 Winding multiplier coils

Coils for multipliers are wound from fine resistance wire, or carbon resistors may be used to give the necessary multiplier resistance.

1 Do you think that it is easier to wind multiplier coils than shunt coils?

A voltmeter which has a number of ranges could be constructed from a milliammeter. A rotary switch (as used in fig. G6.3) is used to switch the appropriate multiplier in series with the meter for the range selected. A circuit for this is incorporated in the design of a multimeter described in Section G12.

G8.5 Experiment: investigating the effect of voltmeter resistance

Assemble the circuit shown in fig. G8.5 on S-DeC or other suitable assembly board.

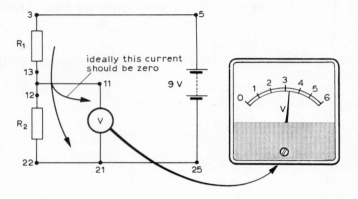

Fig. G8.5 Experimental circuit for finding how an ammeter affects current flow.

a) Make sure that you connect the voltmeter to the circuit correctly.

b) Make sure that the voltmeter has an f.s.d. which is sufficiently high for the battery e.m.f. that you use.

c) R_1 and R_2 should be as nearly equal as possible. Measure the voltage across R_2.

d) Enter the estimated voltage (i.e. 3.0 V) with the actual voltage measured in a table like that shown below.

e) Repeat the observation for R_1 and R_2 each having values of 1 kΩ up to values of 1 MΩ.

R_2 (ohms)	estimated voltage	actual voltage

If the voltmeter were 'perfect' (so that it did not draw any current from the supply), the readings you would obtain would each be 4.5 V, provided there were no inequalities in the resistor values. However, the meter does draw some current, so your results should show that the indicated voltages become smaller as the resistance values are progressively increased. This effect is very marked when the value of R_2 is larger than the resistance of the voltmeter; that is, when the voltmeter begins to draw more current than R_2.

The most important conclusion to this experiment that you should reach is that a voltmeter must have a high resistance if the true voltage is to be measured. As a general rule, it is advisable to choose a voltmeter whose resistance is ten times as great as that of the resistance across which it is placed.

G8.6 Using a voltmeter to measure current

Current strengths can be measured with a voltmeter and a resistor of known value. Suppose you want to know the current through R in fig. G8.6; R is unknown, so measuring the voltage across it (with a high-resistance voltmeter) will not give you the current through it.

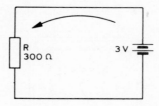

Fig. G8.6 What current flows?

1 What is the current through R in fig. G8.6?

Suppose you connect a known resistance in series with R, such as in the circuit of fig. G8.7. Its value is chosen to be 25 Ω – much less than R. Now measure the voltage across R_1.

2 How will this voltage give you the current?

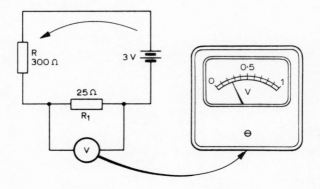

Fig. G8.7 The position for the voltmeter.

3 If introducing R_1 is to have a negligible effect on the current through the circuit, what can you say about R_1?

4 Calculate the new current through R_1.

Thus, if you do measure current in this way, then you **must** use a resistor whose resistance is low compared to other resistors in the circuit placed in series with R or other components in the circuit.

5 What f.s.d. voltmeter would be suitable for this measurement?

6 What is the current through the resistor in fig. G8.8?

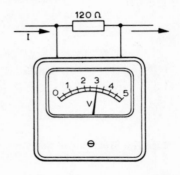

Fig. G8.8 What is the current flowing?

G9 THE COMBINED USE OF AN AMMETER AND A VOLTMETER

G9.1 How the value of a resistor is found

The resistance of a component through which direct current is flowing can be found by using a moving-coil voltmeter and ammeter.

1 What precautions should you take when choosing meters for this measurement?

2 Knowing V and I, how do you calculate R?

G9.2 Circuit 1

Fig. G9.1 shows the connections of a voltmeter and ammeter which you could use for determining the value of an unknown resistor.

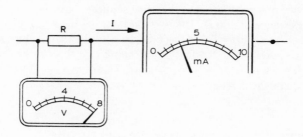

Fig. G9.1 The ammeter measures the sum of the meter and resistor currents.

1 If $V = 8$ V and $I = 3$ mA, what is the resistance of R?

2 Under what conditions does the current through the ammeter equal the current through R?

You will appreciate that the voltmeter may shunt the resistor so that less current flows through the resistor than the ammeter indicates. Suppose the resistance of the voltmeter is the same as the value of R, i.e. 2.7 kΩ, then the current through R is 1.5 mA, not 3 mA. The voltmeter would read 4 V, not 8 V, and the value of R you would calculate would be 1.35 kΩ, not 2.7 kΩ. Thus there would be a 100% error.

G9.3 Circuit 2

Alternatively, you could use the ammeter and voltmeter as shown in fig. G9.2. Now the voltmeter records the sum of the voltages across R and the ammeter.

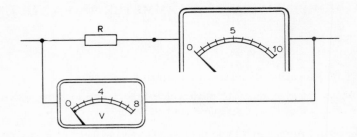

Fig. G9.2 The ammeter measures only the current through the resistor.

1 Does the ammeter measure the true current through R?

Thus, although the true current is now measured, the voltmeter records a rather higher voltage than that across R. How much higher depends on the resistance of the ammeter compared with that of R. Suppose the voltmeter reads 8 V and the ammeter reads 3 mA as before, but this time suppose that the ammeter has the rather high resistance of 200 Ω. Then, again, the total resistance of the ammeter and the resistor (in series) is 2.7 kΩ as measured by the meters, but, since the ammeter has a resistance of 200 Ω, that of the resistor R is (2700 − 200) or 2.5 kΩ, which gives an error in the resistance measurement of 200/27 or 8% too high. For ammeters which have a lower resistance than 200 Ω, the error would be less.

G9.4 Experiment: comparison of the two circuits

Generally, the arrangement of fig. G9.2 is preferable to that of fig. G9.1 for electronic measurements. However, the problem of the voltmeter 'loading' the circuit to which it is connected still remains. This is discussed in Section G10.

Set up the circuits of fig. G9.1 and 9.2. Use a 9 V battery as a suitable source. Let the values of R be 10 Ω, 100 Ω, 1 kΩ, 10 kΩ, and 100 kΩ in turn. For each of these values, make the following measurements.

1 Measure the current and voltage for each circuit, and calculate the apparent resistance in each case.

2 When R is low, which circuit gives the best value for R?

3 When R is high, which circuit gives the best value for R?

G10 THE OHMS-PER-VOLT RATING OF A VOLTMETER

G10.1 Reminder

Before discussing this important characteristic of a voltmeter, fig. G10.1 will remind you, once again, how you connect a voltmeter to measure a voltage. The voltmeter is recording the voltage across the resistor R in a circuit, part of which is shown.

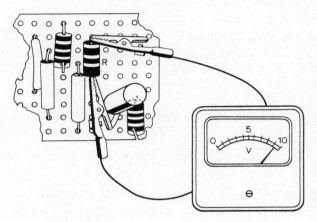

Fig. G10.1 The connecting of a voltmeter.

1 If the current through R is 2 mA, and R has a resistance of 4.7 kΩ, what voltage should the voltmeter record?

However, in the case of fig. G10.1, you may not know if any current is flowing through the voltmeter. The size of this current depends on the resistance of the voltmeter compared with that of the component R.

2 Must the resistance of the voltmeter be high or low compared with that of R if it is not to draw appreciable current from the circuit?

G10.2 Effect of voltmeter resistance

Suppose the voltmeter in fig. G10.1 has a resistance of 4.7 kΩ, the same as that of R.

1 How much current flows through the voltmeter?

Your answer to the last question should be 2 mA. You probably reasoned like this: since the voltmeter has a resistance equal to that of R, then their combined resistance is $(4.7/2)\,k\Omega$. Assuming that the voltage which provides the current through R remains the same, then 4 mA flows: 2 mA through R and 2 mA through the voltmeter. However, your assumption that the voltage available remains the same is unlikely to be true. It is almost certain that the increased current drawn from the circuit will alter the voltage throughout the circuit. The voltmeter will not read the undisturbed value of the voltage, since the operating conditions of the circuit will change. The low-resistance voltmeter is said to 'load' the circuit. This only serves to remind you that a high-resistance voltmeter is required, much higher than that of the resistor across which it is connected, if the circuit conditions are not to be disturbed.

G10.3 The meaning of 'ohms-per-volt'

The *loading effect* of a voltmeter on a circuit is determined by the voltmeter's ohms-per-volt (Ω/V) rating. This is given by

$$\Omega/V = \frac{1}{\text{f.s.d. current}} = \frac{\text{meter resistance}}{\text{f.s.d. voltage}}$$

Thus a meter which has an ohms-per-volt rating of $1\,k\Omega/V$ requires 1 mA to give full-scale deflection.

1 What is the ohms-per-volt rating of an instrument which gives an f.s.d for a current of $100\,\mu A$?

The higher the Ω/V rating, the less the meter 'loads' the circuit. The ohms-per-volt rating of a meter is independent of any multiplying resistors used to extend the range. For example, if the $1\,k\Omega/V$ meter is converted to read 10 V f.s.d., then the multiplier resistance required is $10\,k\Omega$, but the meter still has the same Ω/V rating. However, in this case the meter will not load the circuit to the same extent as it would on a lower voltage range. The higher the ohms-per-volt rating, the more delicate and expensive the instrument. Fortunately, electronic voltmeters are available with Ω/V ratings greater than $1\,M\Omega/V$.

G10.4 Measuring electron-moving force (e.m.f.)

A high-resistance voltmeter is necessary when e.m.f. is being measured.

1 Can you remember the definition of e.m.f.?

Since no current should be drawn from a battery or cell or power supply if its e.m.f. is being measured, a high-resistance voltmeter is necessary. If current is drawn, then the voltage actually measured is always less than the e.m.f. The trouble arises because of the internal resistance of the source. When current is drawn from the source, the current also flows through the internal resistance of the source.

Fig. G10.2 shows a low-resistance voltmeter connected to a 22.5 V battery; that is, the e.m.f. is 22.5 V, and this is what is usually marked on the battery.

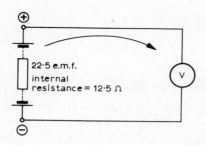

Fig. G10.2 The effect of internal resistance.

Current flowing through the source also flows through the internal resistance; thus the voltmeter reads the e.m.f. less the voltage across the internal resistance.

2 What would the voltmeter read in fig. G10.2 if the internal resistance of the battery is 12.5 Ω and the resistance of the voltmeter is 100 Ω?

Your answer to the last question should be 20 V, obtained as follows. The total series resistance is 112.5 Ω, and the total e.m.f. in the circuit is 22.5 V; therefore the current in the circuit is 22.5/112.5 = 0.2 A. Therefore the voltage across the internal resistance is 0.2 × 12.5 = 2.5 V. Since 2.5 V is the voltage across the internal resistance, the voltmeter reads the 20 V which remains across the terminals.

G11 THE OHMMETER

G11.1 The principle of an ohmmeter

So far you have seen how a moving-coil milliammeter or microammeter can be used to measure currents and voltages. Such an instrument can also be converted to read ohms. To see how this is done, look at fig. G11.1, which shows a current of 1 mA flowing through a circuit.

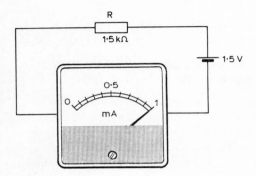

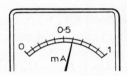

Fig. G11.1 Full-scale-deflection current.

Fig. G11.2 Lower current for a high resistance.

1 Show that the current is 1 mA.

The meter in fig. G11.1 reads f.s.d. because it is calibrated 0–1 mA. Suppose that you knew the supply voltage was 1.5 V, as shown, but not that the value of R was 1.5 kΩ. Working the calculation with V and I known would give $R = 1.5$ kΩ. Similarly, if the indicated current were 0.47 mA, then R would have been 1.5 V/ 0.7 mA = 3.2 kΩ.

2 What would R have been if the milliammeter reading were as indicated in fig. G11.2?

In a similar way to the last calculation, you could find the resistance corresponding to currents of 0.1, 0.2, 0.3, ... to 1 mA and mark the resistance values on the dial of the instrument to give you an ohmmeter. There is, however, a practical drawback to this simple instrument.

3 Can you think what this drawback might be?

4 What would happen if R were less than 1.5 kΩ?

G11.2 Overcoming the problem of the simple ohmmeter

The answer to the last question is that the needle of the meter would be at greater than f.s.d. and there is a possibility of damage to the meter. There is a simple remedy to this problem. The solution is to connect a resistor which is permanently in series with the meter.

1 Suppose with the circuit of fig. G11.1 you were to connect a resistance in series with R. Would the meter deflection increase or decrease?

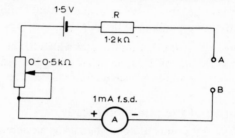

Fig. G11.3 A complete simple-ohmmeter circuit.

To see how this permanently-connected resistor works, look at fig. G11.3. Two resistors are shown in series with the 1.5 V supply and the 0–1 mA meter (it is assumed that the ammeter has a negligible resistance). One of these resistors has a fixed value of 1.2 kΩ, and the other one is variable of value 0.5 kΩ maximum. Suppose the terminals A and B are short-circuited with a piece of wire. The variable resistor is then adjusted so that the meter reads f.s.d. This reading then corresponds to no resistance between A and B. Now suppose that the short-circuit is replaced by a resistance of 100 Ω, as in fig. G11.4.

2 What will happen to the current?

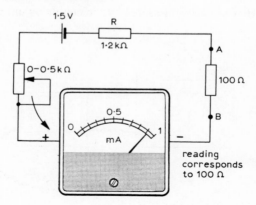

Fig. G11.4 The effect of measuring a resistance with the simple-ohmmeter circuit.

31

G11.3 The 'odd' nature of the ohms scale

You will agree that, as progressively higher resistor values are placed between A and B, the current becomes smaller and smaller. The higher the resistance across AB, the greater the deflection of the needle towards the left-hand side of the scale. The scale can then be marked in ohms corresponding to each of the known resistor values across AB.

1 Note that the resistance scale is in the reverse direction to the amperes and volts scales. What resistance between A and B would bring the needle to the position exactly corresponding to 0 mA?

2 Examine an Avometer or other multimeter which has an ohms scale. Apart from the reverse reading of the scale, what other difference between the ohms and the volts or amperes scale do you notice? Can you explain this?

G11.4 The polarity of the ohmmeter leads

One of the most important points to note when using an ohmmeter concerns the polarity of the leads. For d.c. current and voltage measurements, you will remember that conventional current must flow into the + terminal of the meter; but for resistance measurement the meter is provided with its own supply (the internal battery). As you will see from fig. G1.4, current is flowing through the meter and *out* of terminal B. Thus B is positive with respect to A, even through B is connected to the negative terminal of the meter.

1 Check the polarity of the leads of an ohmmeter with the circuit shown in fig. G11.5. Switch a multimeter to the 'ohms × 1' range. Use another multimeter, switched to volts, or a separate voltmeter (0–10 V) to show that the *red* lead of the multimeter has a *negative* polarity when switched to 'ohms' ranges.

2 What resistance is being measured by the ohmmeter in fig. G11.5?

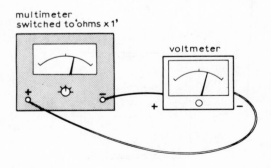

Fig. G11.5 Using an ohmmeter to measure the resistance of a voltmeter.

G11.5 Continuity testing with an ohmmeter

One of the most common uses of the ohmmeter is to check for 'continuity' in a circuit. For instance, you might suspect that a fuse has blown. To test the fuse, you could easily connect it across the terminals of an ohmmeter. A very small resistance would indicate that the fuse had not blown.

    1 Which end of the scale would the needle be if the fuse had blown?

Fig. G11.6 shows a bunch of wires twisted together to form a cable. The problem is, how do you find the lower cable ends which correspond to the upper ends? The cables may be coloured, and this would give you a clue. This matching of colours is what you do when using mains cable to connect a piece of apparatus to a plug or socket — you assume that the same coloured ends belong to the same piece of wire. However, the colours may have faded, or the wires may not be marked. As shown in fig. G11.6, an ohmmeter can be used to find the correct ends without any doubt. The crocodile clip is attached to each lead in turn, until the pointer of the meter swings over to the right, indicating a low resistance.

    2 What would you conclude if the meter indicated an open-circuit on all leads?

    3 What would you conclude if, with one clip attached to a lower wire, two of the upper wires gave a zero reading?

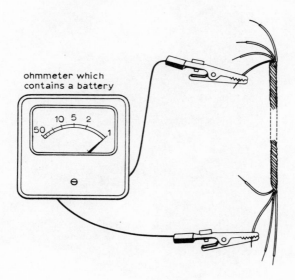

Fig. G11.6 A continuity test using an ohmmeter.

G12 BUILDING A MULTIMETER

G12.1 The basis of a multimeter

A meter which is capable of measuring a number of electrical quantities using the same basic movement is known as a *multimeter*. There are many types of multimeter based on a moving-coil movement, and you should refer to Section B for an illustration of some types.

1 What do the letters, 'A', 'V', and 'O' stand for in 'Avometer'?

The most important part of a multimeter is a sensitive moving-coil milliammeter or microammeter. Using the knowledge that you have gained in this chapter, it is possible with care and patience to construct a multimeter with which a number of electrical quantities can be measured accurately and which you will find very useful in electronic-circuit testing. The following notes outline the construction of the multimeter shown in fig. G12.1.

Fig. G12.1 A 'home-made' multimeter.

34

G12.2 Calculating shunt and multiplier values

The meter used in the construction of this multimeter has a 1 mA f.s.d. scale. It is easy to calculate that this means that it has a sensitivity of 1 kΩ per volt (Section G10.3). The coil of this instrument has a resistance of about 62 Ω, so that when 1 mA flows through it at f.s.d. the voltage across the coil is 62 mV. Knowing this resistance, you will be able to answer the following questions.

1 Calculate the value of the shunt resistors required to convert the meter to one reading 10 mA and 100 mA f.s.d.

2 Calculate the multiplier resistances required to convert the meter to one reading 1 V, 10 V, 25 V, 50 V, 100 V, 250 V and 500 V f.s.d.

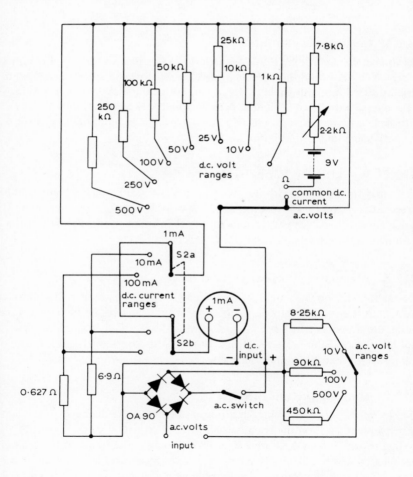

Fig. G12.2 The 'home-made' multimeter circuit.

35

You can check your answers to these questions from the circuit diagram of the multimeter shown in fig. G12.2. Note that the values on the circuit are approximate, since, as you assemble the multimeter, each scale will be calibrated against the readings of a reliable multimeter.

G12.3 Constructing multipliers

The multipliers are chosen from carbon or, better, wire-wound resistors. Thus, from a stock of resistors, a 1 kΩ value is selected which will give an f.s.d. of 1 V; from a selection of these 1 kΩ resistors, at least one should have the correct value to give f.s.d. with 1 V across the meter terminals. Alternatively, you could solder resistors in series or parallel until you have the correct value.

G12.4 Constructing shunts

The shunts are made from 36 s.w.g. eureka wire (see Section G6.2) on a suitable former. You may wind the coils on high-value resistors and adjust the length of wire until f.s.d. is obtained with 10 mA and 100 mA across the meter terminals. If the eureka wire is not insulated, then it should be wound carefully or coated with shellac so that adjacent coils do not touch. Finally, you should protect the coil with some kind of insulation tape.

G12.5 Providing an 'ohms' scale

Ohms may be measured with this meter. A 9 V internal battery is connected in series with a fixed 7.8 kΩ resistor, a 2.2 kΩ variable resistor, and the meter. The variable resistor enables you to adjust the scale reading on short-circuit of the terminals so that the meter reads 0 Ω (see Section G11).

G12.6 Alternating-current voltage ranges

The instrument shown in fig. 12.1 also has a.c. voltage ranges. For this purpose the a.c. must be rectified to d.c. before the current can operate the meter. Four diodes are shown in a bridge circuit to provide the rectified current, but the multipliers have values different from those for the corresponding d.c. ranges of voltage. Note that this simple meter does not have a.c. current ranges.

G12.7 Housing the multimeter

The size of the wooden cabinet depends on the depth and diameter of the meter, principally, and not on the circuit size. The approximate dimensions of the cabinet shown in fig. G12.1 are 250 X 180 X 70 mm. The frame of the cabinet was rebated within 20 mm of the top edge, and the corners were mitred. It was then treated with three coats of polyurethane polish and burnished to an egg-shell gloss.

ANSWERS TO QUESTIONS – Section G

1.1.1   Read on.
Yes – read on.

2.1.1   You may find that the units are watts or wind speed or any measurable quantity which can be converted into a current and made to operate a meter.

2.1.2   The wire is nearly always enamelled copper, often very fine and wound on an aluminium former.

2.1.3   By the controlling springs, *not* by the bearings.

2.1.4   To exert a controlling force on the coil and to take the current in and out of the coil.

2.1.5   Clockwise as you look at the face of the meter.

2.1.6   Generally horseshoe shaped. The pole pieces are soft iron, shaped so as to concentrate the magnetic field through the coil and make the field radial.

2.1.7   To compensate for changes in the zero reading caused by maltreatment producing, for instance, a bent needle or distorted springs.

2.2.1   The twisting forces of the spiral springs

2.2.2   You may not be able to work this out unless you have done some experiments, but the coil would rotate until it was perpendicular to a line joining the pole-pieces.

2.2.3   Could be, but see Sections 2.3 and 12.6.

3.2.1   Electrons.

3.3.1   'Potential difference' or 'voltage across', but not just 'potential' or 'voltage'

3.2.2   Low resistance

3.3.2   High resistance

4.2.1   0.75 mA. Use $I = V/R$.

4.2.2   3 V

4.3.1   4.05 kΩ

4.3.2   0.74 mA

4.3.3   0.74 mA

4.3.4 $V = I \times R = 4 \times 0.74 = 2.96 \, V$

4.4.1 $(1/1\,000\,000)A$ or 10^{-6} A; $(1/1000)A$ or 10^{-3} A

4.5.1   The black $(-)$ terminal, since this is leading to the negative terminal of the battery.

5.1.1   0.5 mA

5.1.2   The coil or springs may melt and break.

5.1.4   1 A f.s.d.

5.2.1   Parallel

5.2.2   Same

5.2.3   The lower-value one

5.2.4   Yes. You must arrange for most of the current to flow through the shunt by connecting a suitable resistor across the terminals of the meter.

5.2.5   Read on.

5.3.1   Very nearly $(1/50)\,\Omega$ – actually $(1/49.98)\,\Omega$

5.3.2   Multiply each scale reading by 5/2 and read as amperes.

6.3.1   To reduce the resistance of connecting leads compared with that of the coil

6.4.1   Three: 1 mA, 10 mA, 100 mA

6.4.2   For the 1 A range, 0.1 Ω; for the 10 A range, 0.01 Ω

7.1.1   Read on.

7.2.1   600 Ω

7.2.2   5 mA

7.2.3   200 mV

7.2.4 $R_T = R_1 \, R_2 / (R_1 + R_2) = 40 \times 40/80 = 20 \, \Omega$

7.2.5   Read on.

8.1.1   Equivalent resistance of R_2 and the meter = $(100/3)\,\Omega$. Total resistance in the circuit = $(1780/3)\,\Omega$. Current in the circuit = $(9/1780)$ A
Voltage across R_2 = (equivalent resistance of R_2 and meter) $\times$ 9/1780
$$= (100 \times 9)/(1780 \times 3)$$
$$= 170 \, mV$$

8.2.1	a) Across R_1, $(9/101)$ V; across R_2, $(900/101)$ V
	b) Across R_1, $(9/11)$ V; across R_2, $(90/11)$ V
	c) Across R_1, $(1000/1001)$ V; across R_2, $(9/1001)$ V

8.3.1 $5 \times 40 = 200\,\text{mV}$

8.3.2 $10 - 200/1000 = 9.8\,\text{V}$

8.3.3 5 mA, same as through the meter

8.3.4 $R = V/I = 9.8/5 \times 10^{-3} = 1960\,\Omega$

8.3.5 Voltage across the meter to give f.s.d. = $100 \times 1 = 100\,\text{mV}$ or 0.1 V
Voltage across the multiplier = $10 - 0.1 = 9.9\,\text{V}$
Multiplier resistance = 9.9 V/1 mA = 9.9 kΩ
Multiply the scale readings by 10 and read as volts.

8.4.1 It is easier, using manganin or eureka wire, to obtain the correct resistance and to measure this resistance, and not so much care need be taken to use low-resistance connecting wire as for shunts. However, if many turns are required, it can be a tedious process.

8.6.1 $I = V/R = 3/300$ A, or 10 mA

8.6.2 By using I = voltage/resistance

8.6.3 R_1 must be much less than R.

8.6.4 $I = 3/325$ or slightly less than 10 mA

8.6.5 One having a f.s.d. slightly greater than $I \times R$ or (10×25) mV; that is, a 250 mV.

8.6.6 $I = (3/120)$ A, or 25 mA

9.1.1 They must be capable of recording the current and the voltage without indicating more than f.s.d.

9.1.2 $R = V/I$

9.2.1 $R = 8\,\text{V}/3\,\text{mA} = 2.7\,\text{k}\Omega$ (approx)

9.2.2 If the resistance of the voltmeter is at least 10 times the resistance of R.

9.3.1 Read on.

9.4.1 Your actual values depend on the resistance of the voltmeter that you use, the e.m.f. of the battery, and the values of the resistors.

10.1.1 $V = I \times R = 9.4\,\text{V}$

10.1.2 High

10.2.1 Read on.

10.3.1 $1/(100\,\mu A) = 10^6/100 = 10^4\ \Omega/V$, or $10\,k\Omega/V$

10.4.1   The e.m.f. is the voltage across the terminals of a source when it is on open-circuit.

10.4.2   Read on.

11.1.1 $I = V/R = 1.5\,V/1.5\,k\Omega = 1\,mA$

11.1.2 $R = 1.5\,V/0.6\,mA = 2.5\,k\Omega$

11.1.3   The drawback is that, if a resistance less than that which gives f.s.d. is placed in the circuit, then the meter movement may be damaged, which is the answer to the next question.

11.2.1   Decrease, since the total resistance in the circuit is increasing.

11.1.2   Read on.

11.3.1   An infinitely high resistance; that is, with the terminals open-circuited

11.3.2   You will notice that, at the higher-resistance end of the scale, the resistance readings are cramped together. The scale is not linear. This is caused by the inclusion of a fixed resistor in the circuit; whereas in the simple ohmmeter of fig. G11.1 the scale is linear.

11.4.2   The resistance of the voltmeter

11.5.1   The left-hand end

11.5.2   That all the leads had broken

11.5.3   That two of the wires were short-circuiting in the cable

12.1.1   Amperes, Volts, and Ohms

12.2.1 and **12.2.2**   See fig. G12.2.

REVISION QUESTIONS – Section G

1 A moving-coil meter makes use of the magnetic field produced by a flow of electrons.
      True? / False?

2 The maximum reading on a meter is known as . . . . (f.s.d.).

3 When a meter is said to have a 'linear' scale, it means that the scale graduations are . . . .
      cramped together at the lower end? / spaced widely apart? / equally spaced?

4 A voltmeter is used for measuring potential difference.
      True? / False?

5 An ammeter measures . . . .
      electric current? / resistance? / voltage?

6 Voltmeters are placed in . . . . with a component across which the voltage is being measured in a circuit.
      series? / parallel?

7 A moving-coil ammeter should have a . . . . resistance.
      high? / low? / medium?

8 The best voltmeters require a high current to operate them.
      True? / False?

9 A 3.3 kΩ resistor has a current of 2 mA flowing through it. Which voltmeter would be most suitable for measuring the voltage across the resistor?
      50 V f.s.d.? / 6 V f.s.d.? / 8 V f.s.d.?

10 In order to convert a milliammeter to one which reads amperes, a . . . . is required.
      battery? / voltmeter? / shunt resistor?

11 The purpose of the shunt across a basic meter movement is to . . . .
      increase the meter resistance?
      increase the current range of the instrument?
      encourage more current to flow through the coil of the movement?

12 a) What is the current which flows through the shunt resistor R in the diagram below if the meter reads f.s.d.
      1.005 A? / 855 A? / 9.95 A? / 995 mA?

  b) Which of these values would you choose for R?
      0.201 Ω? / 0.025 Ω? / 0.402 Ω? / 0.415 Ω?

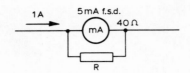

13 A meter movement requires a current of 5 mA to give f.s.d. and has a resistance of 500 Ω. What is the value of the shunt resistor required so that there is an f.s.d. of (a) 10 mA? (b) 1 A? (c) 3 A?

14 The movement of a moving-coil meter has a full-scale voltage drop of 0.5 V and an internal resistance of 1 kΩ. What is the value of the shunt resistor required to convert this instrument to one reading to (a) 2.5 A? (b) 100 mA? (c) 3 A?

15 A multiplier resistor is used to . . . .
    decrease the range of an ammeter?
    increase the accuracy of the voltmeter?
    extend the range of a voltmeter?

16 What is the value of R so that the meter in the diagram below reads f.s.d.?
    800 Ω? / 450 Ω? / 400 Ω? / 360 Ω?

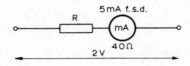

17 A meter movement requires a current of 50 μA to give f.s.d. and has a resistance of 500 Ω. What is the value of the multiplier required to cause f.s.d. for a voltage of (a) 1 V? (b) 5 V? (c) 100 V?

18 A voltmeter uses a meter movement which has an internal resistance of 1 kΩ and an f.s.d. voltage drop of 0.5 V. What is the value of the multiplier resistor required to convert this meter to one reading to (a) 1 V? (b) 50 V? (c) 200 V?

19 What is the value of the current flowing through the resistor in the diagram below?
    0.4 A? / 40 mA? / 480 mA?

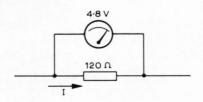

20 The ohms-per-volt rating of a voltmeter is equal to the . . . .
full-scale voltage? / internal meter resistance? / reciprocal of the full-scale current?

21 A voltmeter uses a meter movement with a $100\,\mu A$ f.s.d. What is the ohms-per-volt rating of the instrument.
$320\,\Omega$? / $10\,k\Omega$? / $25\,k\Omega$? / $1\,\Omega$? / $3.8\,k\Omega$?

22 The ohms-per-volt rating of a meter is a measure of the loading action a voltmeter will place on a circuit.
True? / **False**?

23 An ohmmeter . . . . employ an internal source of voltage.
does? / does not?

24 The ohmmeter scale is linear.
True? / False?

25 The function of the ohms-adjust control on an ohmmeter is to . . . .
compensate for battery change?
compensate for internal component-value change?
to convert the meter to an ammeter?
compensate for both component and battery change?

26 When an ohmmeter is measuring zero ohms . . . .
no current flows through the movement?
maximum current flows through the movement?
the terminals are on open-circuit?

27 A $50\,\mu A$ f.s.d. meter with a movement of resistance $5\,k\Omega$ is to read f.s.d. when the leads are shorted. What value should the ohms-adjust rheostat have if the internal battery e.m.f. is 1.5 V?
$30\,k\Omega$? / $25\,k\Omega$? / $5\,\Omega$?

REVISION ANSWERS – Section G

1 True

2 Full-scale deflection

3 Equally spaced

4 True

5 Electric current

6 Parallel

7 Low

8 False.

9 8 V f.s.d.

10 Shunt resistor.

11 Increase the current range of the instrument

12 (a) 995 mA; (b) 0.201 Ω

13 (a) 500 Ω; (b) 2.15 Ω; (c) 0.25 Ω

14 (a) 250 Ω; (b) 5.03 Ω; (c) 0.167 Ω

15 Extend the range of a voltmeter

16 360 Ω

17 (a) 19.5 kΩ (b) 100 kΩ, (c) 2 MΩ

18 (a) 1 kΩ, (b) 99 kΩ, (c) 399 kΩ

19 40 mA

20 The reciprocal of the full-scale current

21 10 kΩ

22 True   23 Does

24 False

25 Compensate for both component and battery change.

26 Maximum current flows through the movement

27 25 kΩ

Section H
Voltage-dividers

H1 INTRODUCTION

H1.1 How resistance and voltage are related

In the previous circuits that you have used, the power source had a fixed e.m.f.
Of course, you could increase or decrease the e.m.f. of the source by adding to or
subtracting from the number of cells or batteries connected together.

1 Do you connect batteries in series or parallel if you want to increase the
e.m.f.?

The disadvantage of this method of changing the voltage for a lamp, say, is that
it can be accomplished only in steps. That is, you can only add to or subtract
from the supply e.m.f. in multiples of the e.m.f.'s of the cells or batteries used.
However, a *voltage-divider* enables you to obtain any voltage up to the maximum
of the supply e.m.f. solely by means of changes to resistor values. To see how this
is achieved with a voltage-divider, look at fig. H1.1 and answer the following
questions.

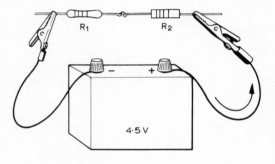

Fig. H1.1 What is the voltage across each resistor?

2 If $R_1 = R_2 = 500\,\Omega$, what is the current flowing through and the voltage
across R_1 and R_2 separately?

3 If $R_1 = 700\,\Omega$ and $R_2 = 300\,\Omega$, is the current the same or different? What
is now the voltage across R_1?

Look at fig. H1.2.

4 What must be the value of R_2 if the voltage across the points X and Y is
1 V?

Suppose in fig. H1.2 you wish to vary the voltage across X and Y while drawing
the same current from the battery.

46

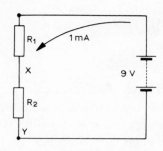

Fig. H1.2 A voltage-divider circuit.

5 What can you say about the sum of R_1 and R_2 if the current is to be constant?

H1.2 Experiment: proving voltage is proportional to resistance

Set up the circuit of fig. H1.2 using values of R_1 and R_2 such that their sum equals 1 kΩ. Connect a high-resistance voltmeter across R_2; that is, one which has a high resistance compared with the resistance of R_2. Measure the voltage between X and Y for different values of R_2, but always ensure that $(R_1 + R_2)$ equals 1 kΩ, so that the current drawn from the battery is constant, that is, it does not change as R_1 and R_2 change.

In your experiment, you will be using R_1 and R_2 arranged as a voltage-divider, so that increasing the value of R_2 increases the voltage differences across it, provided the source current remains constant. This is a device which while drawing a constant current from a source, produces a variable voltage between two of its terminals. Note down corresponding values of R_2 and the voltage across it. What do you notice about them?

H2 THE POTENTIOMETER

H2.1 Potentiometers have three terminals

Previously you have used a variable resistance to control the current to a lamp, say, by connecting it in series with the lamp and the supply. Although the variable resistance probably had three terminals on it, you only required two of them — the one connected to the *wiper* and one of the *end terminals* to the resistance wire or resistance material. The latter is usually a carbon-composition material.

H2.2 Some types of potentiometers

The potentiometer makes use of all three terminals, so that a variable voltage can be obtained from a fixed supply voltage. Fig. H2.1 shows a *preset* potentiometer

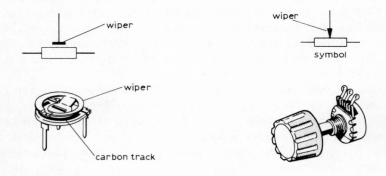

Fig. H2.1 A preset potentiometer —
            horizontal mount.

Fig. H2.2 A spindle potentiometer.

and its symbol; the preset type is adjusted with a screwdriver. Fig. H2.2 shows the kind of potentiometer which requires a knob to adjust the position of the wiper. Fig. H2.3 is a diagram showing the track and wiper of a typical *carbon-track* potentiometer. The track could be made of coiled wire, in which case the potentiometer is called a *wire-wound* potentiometer. Note that the wiper is always connected to the centre tag or terminal — see fig. H2.4.

H2.3 How a potentiometer divides a voltage

Fig. H2.5 shows how a variable resistance of the *coiled-wire* type, and which has three terminals, is wired up to act as a potentiometer. V_i is the input voltage and V_0 is the output voltage.

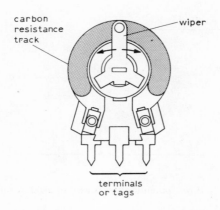

Fig. H2.3 The structure of a potentiometer.

Fig. H2.4 A selection of potentiometers.

1 What is the voltage across tags 1 and 3?

2 What is the voltage across tags 2 and 3 when the wiper is
   a) half-way round from tag 1?
   b) 1/5 of the way round from tag 1?
   c) 2/3 of the way round from tag 1?

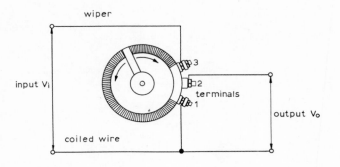

Fig. H2.5 How a potentiometer is used to divide a voltage.

3 What is the position of the wiper when the voltage across tags 1 and 2 is zero?

Thus the potentiometer enables you to obtain any voltage between zero and the e.m.f. of the supply, simply by altering the position of the wiper. A potentiometer is frequently called a *'variable resistance'*, because it is often used as such. It is a bit confusing, but the abbreviation for a potentiometer in circuit diagrams is VR, which refers to 'variable resistance'.

4 Examine some potentiometers. How are they connected in a circuit? What maximum value of resistance do they give?

H2.4 The resistance ranges of potentiometers

Note that potentiometers have maximum resistance values as high as 5 MΩ, usually in the series of values 100 Ω, 200 Ω, 250 Ω, 500 Ω, 1 kΩ, 2.0 kΩ, 2.5 kΩ, 5.0 kΩ, 10.0 kΩ, 20.0 kΩ, etc. The resistance between two terminals for equal angular rotation of the spindle of the potentiometer may increase *linearly* or *logarithmically*. The linear type is the most common; for this type, the resistance increases in direct proportion to the angular position of the wiper. The 'log' type is designed so that equal angular increases in the position of the wiper leads to a logarithmic variation of resistance between two of the terminals.

H2.5 Experiment: seeing how a potentiometer works

Set up the circuit of fig. H2.5 using a 9 V supply and a 250 Ω wire-wound resistor. Use a voltmeter to measure the voltage across terminals 1 and 2 for different positions of the wiper.

1 What are the positions of the wiper for maximum and minimum voltage across terminals 1 and 2?

2 Are your measured results the same as those calculated knowing the supply e.m.f. If not, can you suggest possible reasons for the difference?

Fig. H2.6 shows the symbolic form of fig. H2.5. Note that current flows through the same resistance whatever the position of the wiper, provided no current is drawn from the potentiometer circuit.

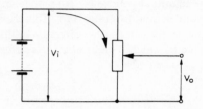

Fig. H2.6 The circuit of a voltage-divider.

H2.6 Experiment: using a potentiometer as a variable resistor

Choose a wire-wound or carbon-track potentiometer. Fit the potentiometer with a knob, so that it is easier to operate it. Switch a multimeter to the 'ohms × 1' range and connect it to the potentiometer as shown in fig. H2.7. Observe the variation of resistance as the knob is rotated.

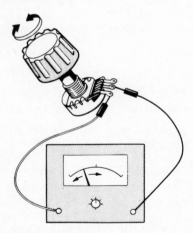

Fig. H2.7 Showing the variable-resistance action of a potentiometer.

1 As you rotate the knob clockwise, does the resistance increase or decrease with the connections shown?

2 Use the ohmmeter to compare the resistance variation of linear and log potentiometers.

H3 EFFECT OF LOAD ON A VOLTAGE-DIVIDER

H3.1 The meaning of a 'load resistor'

The effect of applying the output voltage V_0 from the potentiometer to an external circuit can be understood from fig. H3.1. This shows the voltage across the points X and Y being applied to another circuit – in this case simply a lamp. This lamp has a resistance R, which is said to *load* the potential-divider, since it draws current from it.

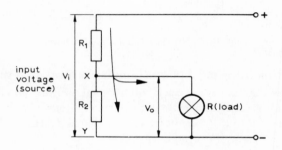

Fig.H3.1 The effect of loading a potentiometer.

1 Is R in series or parallel with R_2?

2 Without R in the circuit, will the currents through R_1 and R_2 be the same?

3 When R is connected, will the current through R_1 be larger or smaller than the current through R_2?

The fraction of the current flowing through R depends on the resistance of R compared with that of R_2.

H3.2 Experiment: seeing the effect of loading a potentiometer

Set up the circuit of fig. H3.1, but use a fixed value for R. First, measure the voltage across XY using a high-resistance voltmeter (at least $10\,k\Omega$) and with R_1 = $100\,\Omega$ and R_2 = $10\,\Omega$. Secondly, measure the voltage across XY when R has values of $1\,\Omega$, $10\,\Omega$, $100\,\Omega$, and $1000\,\Omega$. A supply e.m.f. of $9\,V$ is suitable.

1 What is the current flowing through R_1 and R_2 with R disconnected?

2 What current flows through R_1 for each of the values of R?

3 What current flows through R for the different values of R?

4 What output voltages did you measure across XY for each value of R?

5 Above what value of R is the output voltage constant to within 10%?

Your results should show that, as R increases in value and becomes much larger than R_2, the voltage across R_2 reaches the value it had when R was disconnected.

H3.3   The 'stiff' voltage-divider

Ideally, the load should draw no current from the potential divider, but in practice this condition is rarely achieved, and a compromise is arrived at. A working rule is that the current drawn by the load should be no more than 10% of the current flowing through the voltage-divider.

1 If the current in the load is small compared with the current in the voltage-divider, will the output voltage vary much as the load changes?

Thus the advantage of the load having a high resistance, compared with that portion of the voltage-divider with which it is connected in parallel, is that the output voltage does not change appreciably as the load changes. Such a voltage divider is known as a *'stiff' voltage-divider*.

H3.4   The regulation of voltage-divider

The variation of output voltage with the variation of load current is undesirable. The word *'regulation'* is used to describe the ability of a voltage-divider (and any other voltage source, as a matter of fact) to maintain its output voltage constant under varying load conditions.

$$\text{Regulation} = \frac{(\text{no-load voltage}) - (\text{full-load voltage})}{\text{full-load voltage}} \times 100\%$$

If the output voltage is steady, this ratio is small, and the regulation is good.

1 When is the regulation poor?

2 The voltage across the output terminals of a voltage-divider is 50 V when it is not delivering current. It falls to 48 V when it is delivering maximum current. What is the regulation?

Fig. H3.2 illustrates the use of a stiff voltage-divider; it maintains a constant voltage at the base of a transistor to stabilise the transistor's operating conditions — see Section I 12.

Fig. H3.3 shows a wire-wound resistor. You will see that it has a number of taps which enable the resistor to be used as a voltage-divider.

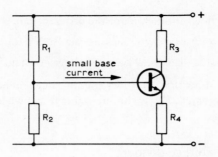

Fig. H3.2 A look ahead to the use of a voltage divider for stabilising the operation of a transistor.

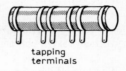

tapping
terminals

Fig. H3.3 A fixed resistor with tapping points.

H4 THE SLIDE-WIRE POTENTIOMETER

H4.1 What is it?

The *slide-wire potentiometer* is a simple apparatus which is used for measuring small differences of voltage. Its special feature is that it does not draw current from the component (e.g. a battery) across which it is connected.

H4.2 Experiment: a demonstration slide-wire potentiometer

Fig. H4.1 shows a simple circuit to set up. Between the terminals A and B mounted at each end of the board, about one metre of 30 s.w.g. constantan wire is stretched. A 9 V battery is then connected across the terminals, the crocodile clips enabling you to connect the battery only when you require an observation. Between A and a sliding contact T, a suitable voltmeter is connected; its range should be larger than that of the e.m.f. of the battery and it should have a high resistance.

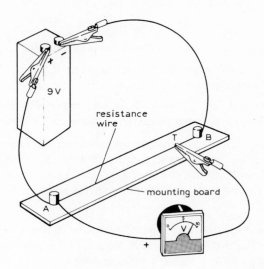

Fig. H4.1 One way of setting up a slide-wire potentiometer.

 1 What happens to the voltmeter reading as you move T from A to B?

If you look back to fig. H2.5, you will notice that that circuit is very similar to fig. H4.1.

 2 Which contact in fig. H4.1 corresponds to the wiper contact of fig. H2.5?

It is instructive to note the readings of the voltmeter for different distances from A to T. Do this, starting with T at the end A and noting the corresponding voltmeter reading. Plot a graph of distance from A against voltmeter reading; the points you obtain will lie close to a straight line, as shown in fig. H4.2.

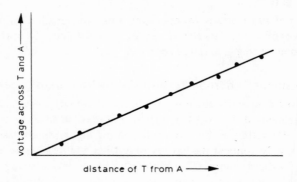

Fig. H4.2 The variation of voltage along the wire.

3 Can you think of a good reason why the points lie on a straight line?

4 What sort of graph would you expect to obtain if the wire became continuously thicker as T moved from A to B?

5 Replace the voltmeter by a 6 V, 0.3 A bulb and confirm that the voltage between A and T becomes progressively higher as T moves from A to B.

Only if the wire is uniform — that is, of constant cross-sectional area and, of course, of uniform material along its length — will the change of voltage along the wire be uniform. Thus this stretched wire, with a constant-voltage source across it, enables a uniformly increasing or decreasing voltage to be selected from it.

6 From your graph, estimate where T should be to give a voltmeter reading exactly half of that when T is at B. Move T to this position and compare the voltmeter reading against your estimation.

7 If you can use a micrometer screw-gauge, measure the diameter of the wire at different positions along it and see whether it is uniform in section.

H4.3 The form of an accurate slide-wire potentiometer

Experiment H. 4.2 should help you to understand how a slide-wire potentiometer works. Fig. H4.3 shows how this kind of potentiometer is used to measure the voltage across the resistor R. The variable resistance 'VR' refers to a rheostat

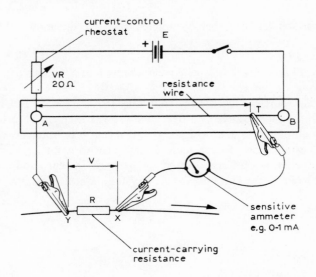

Fig. H4.3· The use of a slide-wire potentiometer to measure a voltage.

which alters the current through the resistance wire AB and hence the voltage across it. Thus VR also limits the current drawn from the *driver* battery E. This reduces the possibility of the e.m.f. of the battery falling during the period of its use, which it is likely to do if the current drawn is too large.

Suppose that, as shown, T is connected to a point along the wire AB so that the voltage across AT is exactly equal to the voltage across R. Then, in the circuit outlined by the points ATXY, the voltage across AT acts to drive current (conventional) anticlockwise round the circuit, while the voltage between X and Y acts to drive current in the reverse, or clockwise, direction. If these voltages are equal, the result is that no current flows through the meter; the meter indicates zero reading – a situation known as '*balancing*'. T is then the *balance point*. If the voltage between A and T is known, then this is also the voltage across R. Notice that the zero reading of the meter means that the potentiometer does not load the circuit of which R is part.

1 Does current continue to flow through R even though the meter reads zero?

2 Which way does the meter deflect if T moves to the right?

H4.4 The use of a standard cell

It is usual to calibrate the wire AB by using a *standard cell* of e.m.f. V_s say. This cell is placed across X and Y, and T is moved to a new position of balance. If l is the length of AT when the unknown voltage is balanced, and l_s the balance point with the standard cell, then by simple proportion the unknown voltage is given by

$$V = V_s \, (l/l_s)$$

The distance along the wire is usually measured by means of a scale in millimetres mounted alongside the wire.

A convenient source of reliable and constant e.m.f. is a *Weston cell;* this produces an e.m.f. of approximately 1.018 V between its terminals. Fig. H4.4 shows how the potentiometer is used with the standard cell. It is extremely important to limit the current drawn from a standard cell, so as to avoid damaging it, and also so that there is not internal drop of voltage in it. The current drawn from the cell is limited by the series resistance, of value about 250 kΩ.

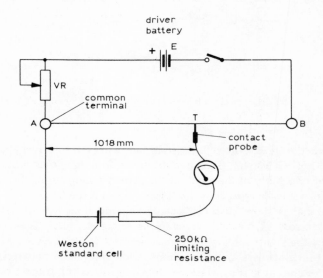

Fig. H4.4 Making use of a standard cell for measuring a voltage.

1 Can you remember the definition of the e.m.f. of a cell?

2 Does it matter whether this limiting resistance is present at balance?

It is possible to calibrate the wire AB so that the distance AT can be directly read in units of voltage. This is carried out as follows.

a) AT is adjusted to be exactly 1018 mm or 1.018 m. This will require the wire to be longer than 1 metre; in fact, 1.50 m would be suitable. T is then placed at this distance from A, and VR is adjusted so that the potentiometer is balanced. This distance then corresponds to 1.018 V.

b) Thus 1 mm of wire corresponds to 1 mV.

58

c) Thus, when V_s is replaced by an unknown voltage (such as V in fig. H4.3), and with VR set to the same value as in (a) above, the length of AT in millimetres (mm) gives V in mV directly.

3 For the adjustments described above, what is the e.m.f. of a cell if a balance point is obtained 1490 mm from A?

The slide-wire potentiometer is ideal for measuring the e.m.f. of a cell, since, by definition, this is the voltage between the terminals when the cell is not delivering current, that is, when it is on open-circuit. Higher e.m.f.'s may be measured by increasing the voltage across the wire.

H5 THE WHEATSTONE BRIDGE

H5.1 Some interesting resistance ratios

Look at fig. H5.1.

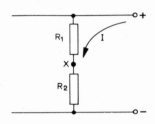

Fig. H5.1 A voltage-divider circuit.

Suppose a) R_1 = 100 Ω and R_2 = 900 Ω, or
       b) R_1 = 10 Ω and R_2 = 90 Ω, or
       c) R_1 = 1 kΩ and R_2 = 9 kΩ, or
       d) R_1 = 500 Ω and R_2 = 4.5 kΩ.

1   What can you say about the voltage at X in each case?

2   What can you say about the ratio $R_1 : R_2$ in each case?

R_1 and R_2 make a voltage-divider. It is always true, for a particular supply voltage, that the voltage at X is constant if R_1/R_2 is constant. Notice that this is true even though the current I is different in each of the cases above.

H5.2 A pair of voltage-dividers makes a Wheatstone bridge

Look at fig. H5.2.

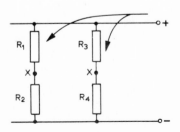

Fig. H5.2 A pair of voltage dividers connected in parallel.

1 Are the two voltage-dividers supplied from the same source?

2 If the voltage at X is to be the same as the voltage at Y, what can you say about R_1/R_2 and R_3/R_4?

3 Under these conditions, will current flow between points X and Y if these points are joined by a wire?

Thus if

$$R_1/R_2 = R_3/R_4$$

then no current flows through the sensitive meter shown in fig. H5.3. This combination of two voltage-dividers, supplied from the same source of e.m.f. is called a *'Wheatstone bridge'*, and this bridge it said to be *'balanced'* when the above equation holds true. Both R_3 and R_4 might have resistance values higher or lower than R_1 and R_2, but, provided that the ratio of these two pairs is the same, the bridge will balance.

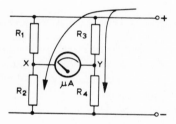

Fig. H5.3 The action of a Wheatstone bridge when it is balanced.

H5.3 How the value of an unknown resistor is measured

Notice that the equation may be written in the form

$$R_1/R_3 = R_2/R_4$$

which is more convenient for the circuits which follow. If R_3 is made 10 times greater than R_1, then the balance occurs if R_4 is 10 times the value of R_2. The ratio of R_3/R_1 is known as the *'multiplying factor'*.

1 Suppose R_4 is unknown, but $R_1 = 10\,\Omega$, $R_3 = 500\,\Omega$, and $R_2 = 40\,\Omega$. What is the value of R_4?

Knowing that the multiplying factor is 50 times, R_4 must be equal to $2000\,\Omega$. Thus the bridge can measure an unknown resistance whose value is greater than that of any other in the bridge. But you will see later that the greatest accuracy in the determination of R_4 occurs if all your resistors are of equal value.

The four resistors make up the four arms of the bridge. However, fig. H5.4 shows an alternative arrangement to fig. H5.3. It is this 'diamond' shape of the

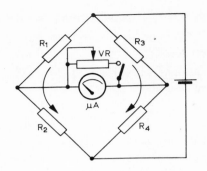

Fig. H5.4 The usual form of a Wheatstone bridge.

four bridge arms which often makes the Wheatstone bridge easily recognisable in circuit diagrams.

2 Are you convinced that fig. H5.4 is the equivalent circuit of fig. H5.3?

In the circuits which follow, the unknown resistor will be placed in the lower right arm of the bridge. The resistor whose value is adjusted so that the bridge balances is then placed in the upper right arm, while the other two arms contain fixed-value resistors. This arrangement of two fixed, one known variable, and the unknown resistance is shown in fig. H5.5.

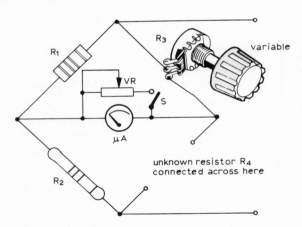

Fig. H5.5 An arrangement for calculating an unknown resistance.

3 Suppose $R_1 = R_2 = 1 \text{ k}\Omega$, and $R_3 = 530 \, \Omega$ when the bridge balances. What is the value of the unknown resistor?

Notice that if the equation is put into the form

$$R_1/R_3 = R_2/R_4$$

you will see directly that R_4 must equal R_3. Thus R_4 has a value of $530\,\Omega$.

 4 Suppose $R_1 = 120\,\Omega$, $R_2 = 480\,\Omega$, and $R_3 = 75\,\Omega$ when the bridge balances. What is the value of R_4?

In order to protect the microammeter from damage when the bridge is un-balanced, a variable resistance VR is connected in parallel with the meter to act as a shunt to the current flowing through it. This is adjusted so that it has a resistance that is low compared with that of the meter when finding the approximate balance of the bridge. The shunt resistance is then increased to make the meter more sensitive while the bridge is exactly balanced. Finally, VR can be switched out of the circuit by means of S.

H5.4 A practical Wheatstone-bridge circuit

Fig. H5.6 shows an arrangement of resistors in a Wheatstone bridge which would enable you to measure an unknown resistance more easily. In this circuit, R_3 is a decade resistance box, from which the total resistance in that arm may be noted easily, instead of having to calibrate the rheostat shown in fig. H5.5. Similarly, the arms containing R_1 and R_2 can be made precise decade values, but not necessarily equal.

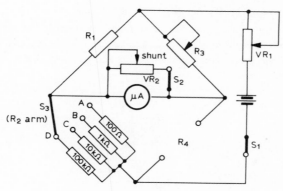

Fig. H5.6 A practical Wheatstone-bridge circuit for measuring resistor values.

Switch S_1 connects the d.c. supply to the bridge, while S_2 switches the shunt VR_2 across the microammeter to reduce its sensitivity for the initial stages of balancing, as described above. The sensitivity of the bridge may also be altered with VR_1.

 1 If VR_1 increases in value, will the bridge become more or less sensitive to changes in the resistance of the arms?

The circuit of fig. H5.6 is capable of measuring up to 1 MΩ in the R_4 arm by using different resistance values switched into the R_2 arm by means of S_3.

In order to measure an unknown resistance R_4, the following procedure is usually adopted.

a) VR_1 is set to maximum and VR_2 to minimum resistance.

b) S_1 and S_2 are closed.

c) R_3 is set to its middle position, and R_1 has a value of 100 Ω.

d) S_3 is switched to position 'A' and, as quickly as possible, R_3 is moved from its maximum to its minimum value, to see whether balance can occur with 100 Ω in the R_2 arm. If balance does occur, VR_2 is increased and VR_1 decreased, and finally S_2 is opened to provide the final, accurate balance. Then, since $R_1/R_2 = 1$, $R_3 = R_4$.

e) If balance does not occur, S_3 is switched to position 'B' (hence $R_2/R_1 = 1000/100 = 10$) and the procedure is repeated as in (d). If balance now occurs, R_4 is ten times the setting of R_3. In this way, R_4 may be as high as 1 MΩ.

2 If the bridge is to balance with $R_4 = 1$ MΩ, what must be the position of S_3 and the value of R_3?

H5.5 Project: an electronic thermometer

Fig. H5.7 shows the Wheatstone bridge arranged to measure the resistance of a thermistor, which you know has a resistance strongly dependent on its temperature. Note that the thermistor is placed in the R_4 arm, but that it has one

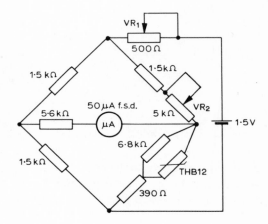

Fig. H5.7 A practical thermistor bridge circuit for measuring temperature.

resistance connected in parallel with it and one resistor in series; their purpose is to enable the meter to give deflections which are proportional to the temperature of the thermistor.

Moreover, with the values of the resistors shown in the bridge arms, the micro-ammeter readings will read degrees Celsius without any need to alter the scale calibrations. VR_1 and VR_2 enable the bridge to be balanced at $0\,^{\circ}C$. As the temperature of the thermistor increases, its resistance decreases, and the out-of-balance current is registered on the meter and read as degrees Celsius.

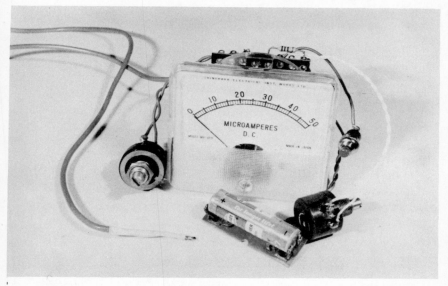

Fig. H5.8 The circuit for an electrical thermometer ready for assembly in a cabinet.

H6 THE MAXIMUM SENSITIVITY OF A WHEATSTONE BRIDGE

H6.1 Factors which influence the sensitivity

One convenient way of looking at the sensitivity of a bridge is to consider it as the change in meter current as the resistance of one arm is increased or decreased. The sensitivity therefore determines the accuracy with which the value of an unknown resistor can be measured. The factors which have to be taken into account when considering the sensitivity of a Wheatstone bridge are:

a) the sensitivity of the meter,

b) the values of VR_1 and VR_2 in fig. H5.6,

c) the value of the supply e.m.f.

However, there is one other very important condition which must be considered. This is the *relative* values of the resistors in the four arms.

H6.2 Experiment: investigating bridge sensitivity

Set up the circuit of fig. H6.1 using resistors of 1% tolerance or less for R_1, R_2, and R_3. A meter of 2 mA f.s.d. and a 4.5 V supply e.m.f. are suitable. The numbers refer to S-DeC, which may be used for connecting the components together.

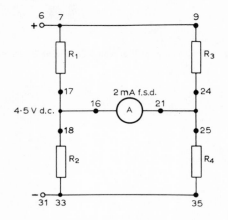

Fig. H6.1 An S-DeC layout of a Wheatstone bridge.

1 With $R_3 = 1$ kΩ, and $R_1 = R_2 = 100\,\Omega$, adjust R_4 until about half f.s.d. is obtained on the meter. Record this reading.

2 Keeping R_3 and R_4 fixed, record the meter deflection in each of the following cases: $R_1 = R_2 = 500\,\Omega; R_1 = R_2 = 5\,k\Omega; R_1 = R_2 = 10\,k\Omega$. For what values of R_1 and R_2 was the deflection greatest?

Your results should show that a bridge must be designed so that the resistances of the arms of the bridge are equal if the maximum sensitivity is to be obtained. This is not always possible or desirable. For instance, in fig. H5.6 R_1 and R_2 were deliberately made unequal so that high resistances could be measured in the R_4 arm with lower-value resistances in the other arms.

3 Suppose $R_1 = R_2 = 100\,\Omega$, and $R_3 = 5000\,\Omega$ at balance. What is the value of R_4 when the bridge is balanced?

4 What values would you choose for R_1 and R_2 in order to make the determination of the balance point more sensitive to the value of R_4?

5 Look at fig. H5.7. Do you think that the bridge is designed to operate near its maximum sensitivity?

Remember that, with all four arms of equal resistance, the bridge could have its greatest sensitivity; but the actual sensitivity depends on the other factors which were noted in Section H6.1.

H6.3   Experiment: do all 1 kΩ resistors have the same value?

The Wheatstone bridge can be used to find the values of a number of carbon resistors, each quoted as 1 kΩ with a 10% tolerance. Set up the bridge as shown in fig. H6.1 using 1% tolerance resistors for R_1 and R_2 and a decade resistance box for R_3, which gives values to at least 1%.

1 What values should these resistors have in order that the bridge will have maximum sensitivity?

Obtain a balance by varying R_3, and so deduce the value of R_4. Record your results as shown in the table. The results are best shown in the form of a histogram, on which the numbers of results in a certain range are indicated. The results in the table give the histogram shown in fig. H6.2. The histogram indicates clearly how the values of the resistors, which have a nominal value of 1 kΩ, vary.

Resistance (Ω)	No. in this range
1050 – 1074	3
1025 – 1049	5
1000 – 1024	3
975 – 999	6
950 – 974	8
925 – 949	7
etc.	

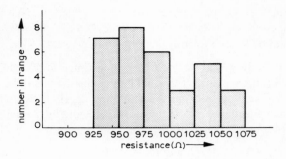

Fig. H6.2 Specimen results from a measurement of the range of values of a 1 kΩ resistor.

2 Would you expect to find that most of the resistors had values close to 1000 Ω?

You will need to test a great many resistors before finding an even distribution about 1000 Ω.

3 Do any of the values you find have a resistance outside the region of 1 kΩ ± 10%?

ANSWERS TO QUESTIONS – Section H

1.1.1 Series

1.1.2 4.5 mA; 2.25 V across each resistor

1.1.3 Same current; 3.15 V

1.1.4 1 kΩ

1.1.5 The sum of R_1 and R_2 must remain constant.

2.3.1 The input voltage V_i

2.3.2 (a) $V_i/2$, (b) $V_i/5$, (c) $2V_i/3$

2.3.3 The wiper will be touching the wire which connects directly to tag 1.

3.1.1 Parallel

3.1.2 Yes

3.1.3 Larger

3.2.1 to These answers will depend on the supply e.m.f. that you use and on the
3.2.5 exact values of the resistors.

3.3.1 See Section H3.4.

3.4.1 When the output voltage varies a lot with the variation of load current.

3.4.2 Regulation = $((50 - 48)/50) \times 100\% = 4\%$

4.2.1 You should find that the voltmeter reading increases in direct proportion
to the distance moved. This means that, if the voltmeter reading is 2 V
at 200 mm, it will be 4 V at 400 mm and 6 V at 600 mm, and so on.

4.2.2 Contact T, the slider contact

4.2.3 The points lie on a straight line if the wire has a constant resistance for
every length of 1 mm, say.

4.2.4 You may find this difficult to work out, but in fact it would vary as in
the diagram on p. 70.

4.3.1 Yes

4.3.2 To the right

4.4.1 It is the voltage across the terminals when the cell is not delivering
current.

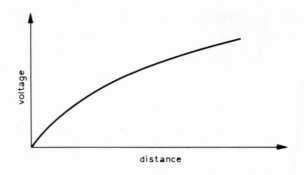

distance

(See answer to question 4.2.4.)

4.4.2 No, but small changes in the position of T may produce damaging deflections of the meter needle.

4.4.3 Since 1 mm of wire corresponds to 1 mV, 1490 mm corresponds to 1.49 V.

5.1.1 Same

5.1.2 R_1/R_2 is constant.

5.2.1 Yes

5.2.2 They must be equal.

5.2.3 No, since current flows between two points in the circuit only if a voltage difference exists between these points.

5.3.1 Read on.

5.3.3 530 Ω

5.3.4 300 Ω

5.4.1 Less sensitive, since this reduces the voltage across the bridge, and hence there are smaller changes of voltage across the meter. However, the balance equation does not alter.

5.4.2 If $R_4 = 1$ MΩ, it is best to make $R_2 = 100$ kΩ. Thus the switch must be changed to position D. Hence, $R_1/R_3 = R_2/R_4 = 100$ k$\Omega/1$ M$\Omega = 1/10$; so $R_3 = 10 R_1 = 10 \times 100 = 1$ kΩ.

6.2.3 5000 Ω

6.2.4 Make $R_1 = R_2 = 5$ kΩ.

6.2.5 Yes, but only when the resistance of the thermistor is about 1.5 kΩ and VR_2 is almost zero. This will occur at high temperatures.

6.3.1   The resistance of each arm should be 1 kΩ.

6.3.2   If a sufficient number are tested, you would expect most to have a value close to 1000 Ω.

1 What is the maximum voltage available across the terminals A and B of the circuit shown? What is the smallest voltage above zero that you could obtain from this series circuit of batteries?

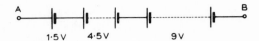

2 What is the voltage across R_2 in the circuit below?

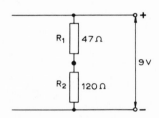

3 A voltage greater than the supply voltage can be obtained from a voltage-divider.
   True? / False?

4 A potential-divider has at least .... terminals.
   none? / one? / two? / three?

5 When a potential-divider is loaded, current is drawn from it by a resistance connected across one part of it.
   True? / False?

6 What is meant by a 'stiff' voltage-divider?

7 The end-to-end resistance of the voltage-divider shown in the circuit opposite is 2.0 kΩ. It is connected to a 9 V source, and the load is taken from the mid-

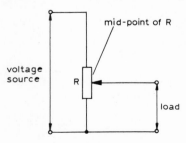